Written by Catherine Zoller
Pictures by Mr. Sketches

RHYME & REASON
SERIES

"GETTING THESE BOOKS IN PEOPLE'S HANDS SO PEOPLE'S HANDS PICK UP THE BOOK."

ABOUT THE AUTHOR

Catherine Zoller is a writer from Tulsa, Oklahoma,
With a husband, three kids and half a college diploma.

Many years ago the Lord spoke to her one night
Saying simply and clearly, "I want you to write."

So she jumped out of bed and grabbed paper and pen
And waited on the sofa for Him to speak to her again.

At last came the dawn with the dew and the mist,
But all she had written was half a grocery list.

Still she never forgot the words spoken that night;
All she had to learn was that His timing's always right.

Now she's written some rhymes that tell the Bible story
From Genesis to Revelation and reveal God's glory.

The hope in her heart is to show everyone
That reading God's word can be lots of fun.

It will instruct you and teach you and change your heart,
And this little book is designed to help you start!

Daniel: The Rhyme and Reason Series by Catherine Zoller
Copyright © 2016 by Catherine Zoller
Printed in Canada

ISBN 978-0-9885122-3-8
For worldwide distribution

Rhyme & Reason Ministries International • P.O. Box 470994 • Tulsa, OK 74147-0994
You can learn more about Catherine Zoller at www.catherinezoller.com

ABOUT THE ILLUSTRATOR

The artist Mr. Sketches is also known by some
As Mr. David Wilson, and he thinks art is fun!

The nickname Mr. Sketches came from a T.V. show
The station TBN broadcast for three years in a row.

His lovely wife named Karen likes to teach the third grade.
They moved 'round a bit, but when they got to Tulsa stayed.

Art from the heart surely helps God's kids succeed,
So when he draws and sketches, this is always David's creed:

"With broad point or with fine or whatever time or season,
It's time to draw the line now, whatever rhyme or reason!"

DEDICATION

This book is dedicated to my husband whom I love;
One of God's greatest gifts to me sent from up above.

We've endured many trials in this journey called life,
But we have triumphed together as husband and wife.

God has always been our source and we look to Him each day,
To lead us and guide us as we follow His sure way.

The faithful prophet Daniel wrote the book that bears his name.
Now there are skeptics out there who'd deny this quite true claim.

The reason for their doubt is God reveals all that He's planned,
And they cannot believe that such a grand thing was at hand.

But those of us who know the Word of God is ever true,
Are not persuaded in the least by what skeptics say or do.

In history this book begins in 605 BC
When Daniel and his friends were taken in captivity.

God's patience was exhausted and would not forever last.
What many prophets promised, well, it finally came to pass.

At last God's righteous judgment came on rebellious Israel.
They'd forsaken Him and then continued to forget Him still.

Jehovah sent an army to invade the Promised Land,
They captured all the nobles, every woman, child and man.

While he was just a teen, Dan was taken to Babylon,
And made to serve in Nebuchadnezzar's court from that day on.

They changed his name and told him to forsake his Father's ways,
But Daniel stayed obedient throughout his many days.

Their faithfulness cost the friends, as we will quite soon see.
Their lives are still a lesson to this day for you and me.

Despite their circumstances in a foreign, pagan land,
Their God was always with them with deliverance at hand.

Now Daniel lived through four kings reigns and served in all their courts.
God gave wisdom, favor, power to him and his cohorts.

He wrote this book to help encourage all the exiled Jews,
Revealing the Lord's plan for them and other wondrous news.

Gather 'round as we recount history and what it means,
And see God's sovereign power at work behind the scenes.

The king of Judah had been reigning
for just three short years,
When the king of Babylon
reduced the Jewish folks to tears.

God Himself had given them
into their enemy's hands,
Because they chose to just ignore
His good and fair demands.

Even after prophets were sent
to warn what He would do,
With a broken heart God finally
said that He was through–

Trying to get them to repent
and look to Him alone.
Rebellion brought on judgment,
and they had to leave their home.

Nebuchadnezzar swooped right in
and gathered up the best,
Including nobles' children
and the temple's treasure chest.

Dan. 1:1-4

7

One of these named Daniel
    was no more than a teen;
Along with him went three dear friends,
    all trained to serve the king.

Their names were changed from godly ones
    to those of pagan gods.
But history proves a mere name change
    would not improve the odds,

That they would turn away and fail
    the true God whom they served.
To bow before a foreign god
    would break with God's true word.

The king provided daily food
    and wine for them to drink,
But Daniel and the other boys
    didn't do as you might think.

Daniel made a pledge that he
    would not defile himself
No matter what they served him
    from the palace kitchen shelf.

Dan. 1:5-8

9

The man in charge of all the eunuchs feared they would look weak,
But Daniel asked for ten days trial to prove their strength would peak.

So they were given water and fresh vegetables to eat.
And at the end of the ten days were strong from head to feet.

God gave these four boys knowledge and wisdom beyond their means;
To Daniel He gave insight into visions and to dreams. Dan. 1:9-13

At the end of their training when they were brought before the king,
He found that there were none like them with such understanding.

These boys were ten times better than the wise men in his realm,
And it would not be long before ol' Dan was at the helm.

Because they would not compromise in even tiny things,
God would soon put them in charge of even greater things! Dan. 1:14-21

In the second year of his reign,
  king Neb, he had a dream.
He tossed and turned because he had
  no clue what it might mean.

The next day it was gone from him, but it still caused him stress,
So he called for sorcerers and magicians and the rest.

"I had a puzzling dream," he said, "Explain it now to me."
"Tell us your dream," the men agreed, "We'll tell you what we see."

The king held firm to what he'd said and told them once again,
To tell the dream and what it meant or he'd kill all of them!

They answered and they said to Neb,
  "What you ask none can do!
There's not a man upon the earth
  to tell your dream to you."

And so their claims to be quite wise
  were shown to be a fraud.
The One who tells us mysteries
  can only be our God.

In a fit of fury the king
  issued his harsh command,
For all the wise men to be killed,
  each one in all the land. Dan. 2:1-13

The captain of the guard came
for Daniel and his friends,
And at that moment it looked like
they'd certainly meet their ends.

With counsel and with wisdom
Daniel spoke up to the guard,
And told him that for his great God
this job was not too hard.

He asked the king to give him time
for God to let him know
The content of the dream
and the message it would show.

He gathered his three friends
and they hit their knees in prayer,
Beseeching the God of heaven,
the dream to them declare.

The secret came to Daniel
in a vision in the night,
And he blessed the God of heaven
who gave him such insight. Dan. 2:14-24

13

Then Daniel went before the king
    and this is what he said,
"Oh king, you had a dream as you
    were lying on your bed.

"There is a God in heaven who
    wants you to understand,
The future that is coming to
    this great and glorious land.

"You saw a giant statue
    and its head was finest gold;
Its chest and arms were silver,
    this you did behold.

"The belly and thighs were bronze,
    and iron made up the legs;
The feet you saw were iron and clay,
    made up of miry dregs.

"In all its awesome splendor,
    the statue before you stood,
When without hands a rock was cut
    and smashed it something good!

"The image was crushed to powder,
    blown like chaff in the wind.
Then the rock, now a mountain,
    filled earth from end to end.

Dan. 2:25-35

14

"And now, oh king, the meaning
    of the dream God has revealed:
The head of gold is you, whom God
    has given beasts and fields.

"Your kingdom of power and might
    has come from His great hand,
But after yours, a lesser king
    will come to rule the land.

"His rule will not be near as grand,
    nor others that will follow,
Each will be inferior;
    this might be hard to swallow.

"The fourth kingdom—iron and clay
    —will break and be divided,
All these things will come about
    because God has decided.

"And after each of these will come
    a Kingdom without end;
Of this you can be certain,
    on this sure truth depend." Dan. 2:36-45

15

Then Ol' Neb fell on his face and acknowledged Daniel's God,
He marveled at such wisdom and for a while was awed.

He showered Dan with gifts; the accolades went on and on,
He made him ruler over all wise men in Babylon.

Who but God would take a man out of the chains he's worn
And set him up as ruler where he wasn't even born?

From history we know quite well the kingdoms talked of here.
That God prewrote some history in Scripture is quite clear. Dan. 2:46-49

16

The first kingdom is Babylon,

the second Medo-Persian;

Third is Greek,

and Rome is fourth,
of that we can be certain.

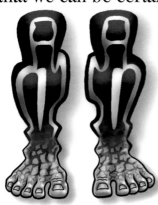

The mixture of the iron and clay
    that we see in the feet
Depicts the weakness that we know
    brought Rome to its defeat.

It's quite important to take note
    Christ's is the fifth kingdom!
And we can read in Acts 2,
    the rule of Christ has come!

The stone that was cut without hands
    is the Kingdom that prevails;
This great and glorious Kingdom all
    the people of God hail.

It wasn't long before Neb's heart
    was puffed again with pride.
He made a giant statue that
    was seen both far and wide.

It towered up toward heaven,
    ninety feet straight in the air.
It was covered with pure gold
    from the feet up through its hair.

He gathered his officials
    from all throughout the land,
To dedicate the statue that
    was built at his command.

The herald cried, "When the music plays
    do as you are told:
You must fall down and worship
    this image made of gold.

"Anyone who fails to fall
    and worship Neb's great power
Will be tossed into a fiery furnace
    within that very hour."

Shadrach, Meshach, Abednego—
    these three refused to bow,
And others who'd been watching them
    were sure they had them now!

Dan. 3:1-7

18

19

They went into the palace saying, "There are certain Jews
Who will not bow before the image made to honor you."

These faithful friends of Dan's were brought before the angry king,
Who gave them one more chance to bow before the graven thing.

"Oh king, we have no need today to tell you where we stand.
We will not bow, and if God wills, He'll save us from your hand.

"But even if He chooses not, let it be known to thee,
We will not worship your false god or follow your decree." Dan. 3:8-18

The furious king screamed out, "Now make it even hotter!"
It seemed their faithfulness to God had put them in hot water.

At Neb's command the fire was stoked; made hotter than before.
The three were bound and soldiers threw them through the furnace door.

The flames had grown so high it killed the soldiers on the spot.
But our three heroes were unharmed; the fire just burned their knots.

Dan. 3:19-22

21

22

The king beheld them walk about, and he just stood there awed.
"Three went in, but I see four! One's like a Son of God!"

This is a vivid picture and God wants us all to trust
That in times of trial and troubles He will always be with us.

So the king, he called them out,
    and they stood there before him.
Not a single hair was singed
    nor smell of smoke upon them.

And then ol' Neb acknowledged God
    and praised the faithful three
For serving first the God they loved
    by defying the decree.

And once again the king spoke up
    and gave God highest praise:
"There is no other god who could
    have saved them from this blaze!"

The trial had passed, and like He does,
    God's favor was restored.
He honored them in all they did
    'cause they lived for the Lord.

A time of peace had come
    to all the people in the land,
And Neb himself declared
    the wonders from God's hand.

Dan. 3:24-30

23

But one night as the king did sleep,
　he had a stranger dream.
Again he called his wise men who
　made up the King's Dream Team.

Yet once more none among them
　could interpret what it meant,
And so he called for Daniel,
　and before the king he went.

"I had a dream in which I saw
　a tree that filled the earth.
Its height was great, its roots were strong,
　it had a mighty girth.

"Abundant fruit upon each branch
　provided food for all.
Creatures rested in the shade,
　and the birds would sing their call.

"Then a holy one from heaven came
　to stand in front of me,
Crying, 'Chop it down, scatter its fruit,
　cause the beasts to flee.

'Let the stump, bound with iron and bronze,
　stay in the grassy ground.
And let him live, drenched in dew,
　where plants and beasts are found.

'Let his heart be changed within
　from that of man to beast,
And seven times pass over him
　before he is released.

24

'That the living know that God Most High
   is sovereign over men.
He gives power to the lowliest
   and sets him over them.'" Dan. 4:1-18

Then Daniel, called Belteshazzar,
   was troubled by a thought;
The first dream dignified the king,
   the second one did not.

You see, Daniel was bothered by
   the meaning of the dream,
And was quite sad to tell the king
   just what the dream would mean.

The king spoke and said, "Belteshazzar,
   don't let it trouble you.
Go on and tell me what it means;
   that's what you now must do."

"The tree you saw which grew so strong,
   O king, the tree is you.
God has a plan to humble you;
   you'll eat grass wet with dew.

"You will be sent away from men
   and you'll live in the wild,
'Til you know it's God who rules
   and are humble like a child.

"God's order to leave the stump
   is gracious and not cruel.
It means your kingdom will come back
   once you accept God's rule."
                              Dan. 4:19-27

25

Just one year later, kids, it happened just as Dan had said.
The king looked out at Babylon and pride filled up his head.

And while he was still bragging about all he'd built and done,
A voice came down from heaven: "You'll be driven out and shunned.

"You will eat the grass like oxen until seven years have passed,
Until you know the Most High rules, and His great truths you've grasped."

That very hour it happened just like God had said it would,
You see, His words are always true, and all His ways are good. Dan. 4:28-37

He humbled Neb and then He helped him understand His ways.
And so the king extolled our God and praised him all his days.

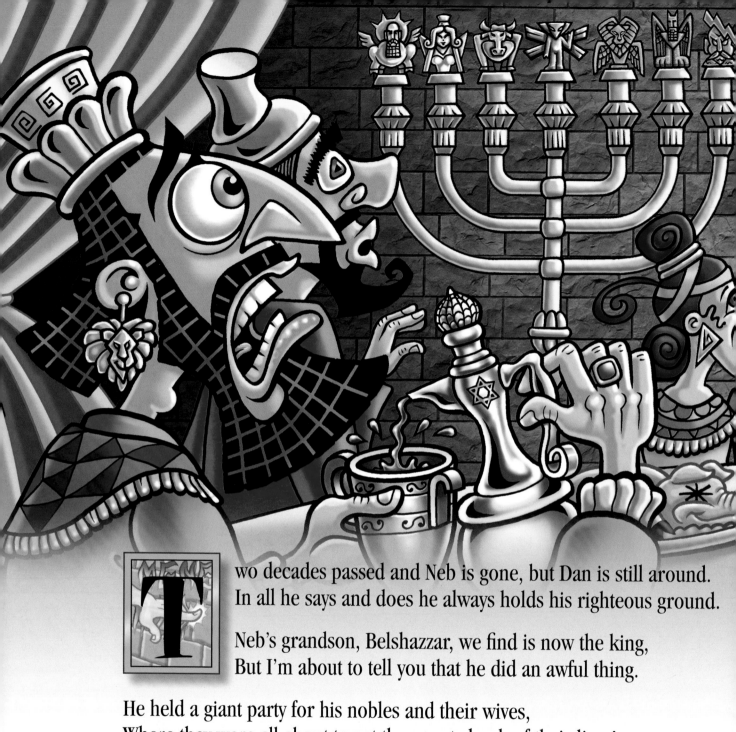

wo decades passed and Neb is gone, but Dan is still around.
In all he says and does he always holds his righteous ground.

Neb's grandson, Belshazzar, we find is now the king,
But I'm about to tell you that he did an awful thing.

He held a giant party for his nobles and their wives,
Where they were all about to get the worst shock of their lives!

Calling for the temple vessels Neb had taken years before,
They drank their wine and praised their gods of wood and stone and ore.

That same hour a hand appeared, writing on the palace wall,
The king's knees knocked, his thoughts went dark, his face it cast a pall.

He cried aloud, "Bring to me now the soothsayers and wise men!
Whoever tells me what this says, I'll give great things to them!"

And just like it has happened in this story twice before,
Not one of them could tell the king the message the wall bore.

Just then the old queen spoke up; she remembered our friend Dan.
She told the king there was a truly wise man in the land. Dan. 5:1-12

29

So Dan was brought before the king
    and promised lots of stuff
If he could tell the meaning of
    the words that seemed so tough.

Daniel answered saying,
    "Keep your gifts, they're not for me."
He then recounted for the king
    his grandpa's history.

Reminding him that Neb was humbled,
    living as a beast,
Daniel gazed around the room
    at ol' King Bel and his great feast.

"You knew the truth, yet didn't let
    it humble your proud heart,
So God has sent a message that
    your kingdom's come apart.

"MENE, MENE, TEKEL,
    UPHARSIN is what is written,
And I'm about to tell you that
    your kingdom will be smitten.

Dan. 5:13-25

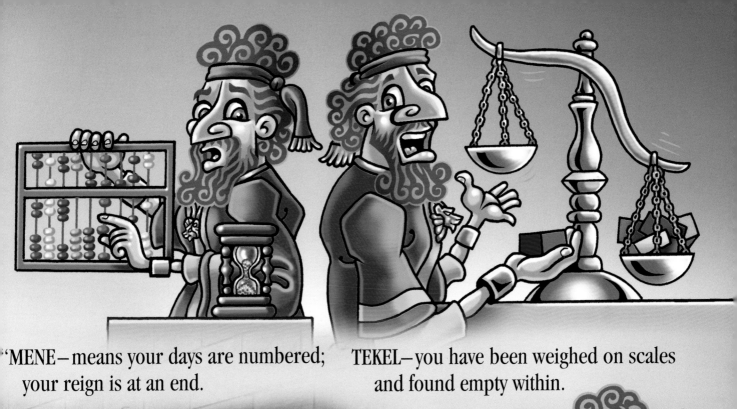

'MENE—means your days are numbered;
your reign is at an end.

TEKEL—you have been weighed on scales
and found empty within.

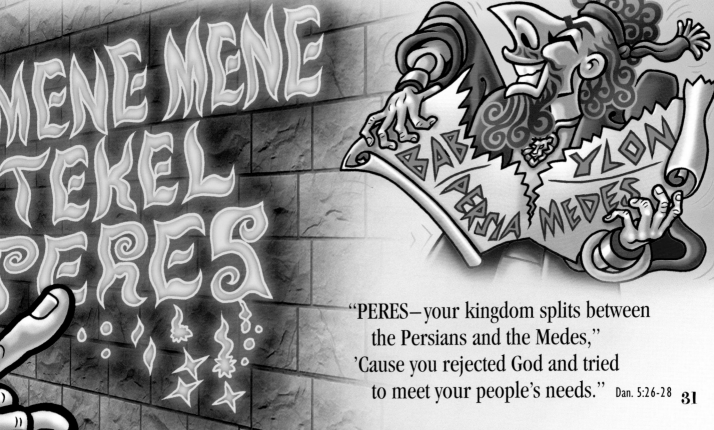

"PERES—your kingdom splits between
the Persians and the Medes,"
'Cause you rejected God and tried
to meet your people's needs." Dan. 5:26-28 **31**

That very night the king was killed just as the words had said,
And Darius the Mede came in and ruled in ole Bel's stead.

Dan. 5:30

The head of gold was gone and now the silver chest would rule,
The kingdom was divided and Belshazzar died a fool.

Dan. 6:1-9

Darius set one hundred twenty princes up to rule,
And over them three governors, of which Dan was the jewel.

As usual Daniel rose above 'cause God had made him wise.
It made the others jealous so they plotted his demise.

They couldn't find a single thing for which they could accuse.
The only trap that they could set was in God's law for Jews.

(Wouldn't it be wonderful
    if it could be said of us:
The only charge that can be made
    is of our faithfulness?!)

And so they went before the king
    and said, "Make a decree
That none should make petitions
    before anyone but thee!

"And if they should within the month,
    oh let it happen then,
That they be thrown alive into
    the hungry lions' den!"

The king, he signed the document,
    and it became a law,
And once a law had been declared
    the king could not withdraw.

Dan. 6:1-9

34

35

When Daniel heard the news, he did just as he'd always done:
He opened up his window, praying toward Jerusalem.

Feeling sure their trap was set, they returned once more and said,
"Oh king, it seems the captive disobeyed the law you read."

Now Darius was quite distraught and tried in every way
To figure out a way that he could save ol' Dan that day. Dan. 6:10-15

Knowing that the law was firm, he could only wait and sit,
While Daniel, faithful one, was thrown into the lions' pit.

But just as God would make a way to rescue fallen man,
He made a way for Daniel to escape the evil plan. Dan. 6:16-17

37

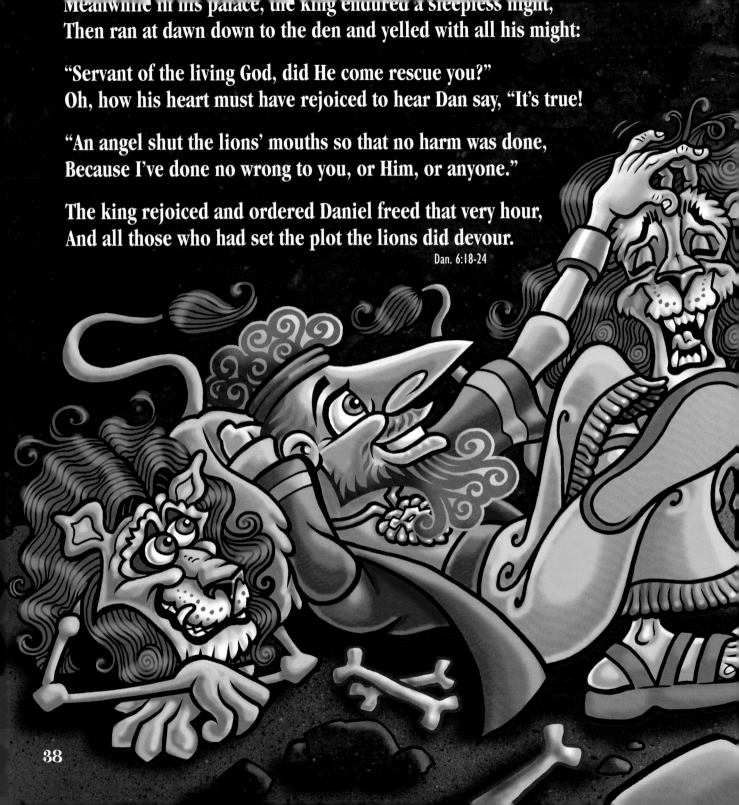

Meanwhile in his palace, the king endured a sleepless night,
Then ran at dawn down to the den and yelled with all his might:

"Servant of the living God, did He come rescue you?"
Oh, how his heart must have rejoiced to hear Dan say, "It's true!

"An angel shut the lions' mouths so that no harm was done,
Because I've done no wrong to you, or Him, or anyone."

The king rejoiced and ordered Daniel freed that very hour,
And all those who had set the plot the lions did devour.

Dan. 6:18-24

39

ourteen years before all this,
  when Belshazzar was still king,
While lying on his bed one day,
  Dan had a vision-dream.

These visions came at different times
  and over several years.
He gathered them together and
  the book now changes gears. Dan. 7:2-

At this point in the book
  things take a very different turn;
No longer history, but dreams
  of prophecy we learn.

Now at these four strange night visions
  we'll take a closer look,
To see all Dan was shown in these
  six chapters of his book.

40

"I saw four winds of heaven
   stirring up from the Great Sea,
Four different beasts came from its depth,
   as different as can be.

"A lion and a bear and then
   a leopard soon appeared,
The fourth like nothing ever seen
   was something to be feared.

"With iron teeth and dreadful strength
   and ten horns on its head,
A small horn rose up, cut off three,
   and spoke vile words of dread."

(The four beasts of his vision
   correspond with Neb's statue.
The four great kingdoms of the earth;
   that much we know is true.)

Dan. 7:2-8

"And then, behold! I saw Him, the one called 'Ancient of Days.'
With fiery throne and flaming wheels and Shekinah glory rays.

"A river of fire flowed; ten thousands attended Him.
The books were opened up," with God's judgment to begin.

"I looked 'cause of the beast's vile words, then watched 'til it was slain;
Its body was destroyed and given over to the flame. Dan. 7:9-12

"Then down came heaven's cloud with someone like the Son of Man,
All dominion was given to Him—people, nations, land."

The mountain that King Neb first saw now filled the entire earth,
And He will rule forever with those of the second birth. Dan. 7:13-14

43

"I, Daniel, was grieved within
and the visions troubled me.
I came near to an angel and asked,
'what is this I see?'

"So he made known the meaning, then,
of all these wondrous things.
'These great beasts, which number four,
are four great earthly kings.

'But the saints of the Most High
will eventually receive
A Kingdom which will come
and it will never, ever leave.'" Dan. 7:15-22

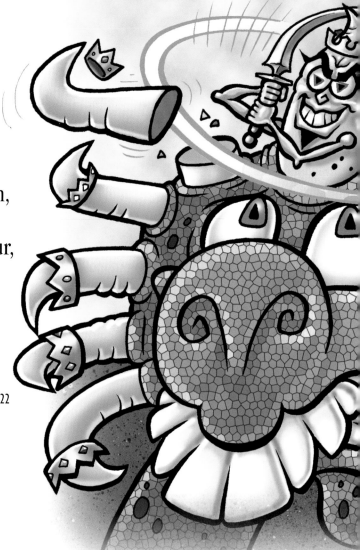

44

Then I desired to know the meaning
of the fourth great beast
Who waged war with the saints
from greatest to the least,

Until the Ancient of Days
judged in favor of His own
And among all the Jews
it came to pass that He was known.

'And then he'll speak against the saints,
    and also God Most High;
To try to change the sacred feasts
    as three more years pass by.

'But the court will sit for judgment
    and his rule will be destroyed,
And the kingdom given to the saints
    who will be overjoyed!'"

These are God-fearing Jews,
    who pass through the tribulation,
Inheriting the promises
    God made unto their nation.

"Thus, he said, 'The fourth beast
    will be a kingdom of the world,
Who will tread the nations down
    as its banners are unfurled.

'The ten horns of this kingdom are
    ten kings that shall arise,
And after them another who
    will cause three their demise.

"And then the vision ended
    and these strange thoughts troubled me;
I felt ill and scared and weak.
    Of these things I didn't speak." Dan. 7:23-28

45

**A**nd then just two years later,
     the year ol' Babylon fell,
Daniel had another vision–
     the future it would tell.

He saw unfold before him
     the next two great empires rise.
The vision also showed him
     their eventual demise.

A voice told Gabriel to explain
     the vision to old Dan,
And when the angel finished,
     Dan fainted and couldn't stand.

He was told to seal up the vision;
     it referred to the final days,
And though it made him sick,
     it also left him quite amazed.

"I read in Jeremiah,
     and began to understand,
The time had nearly come for us
     to go back to our land! Dan. 8:1-9:2

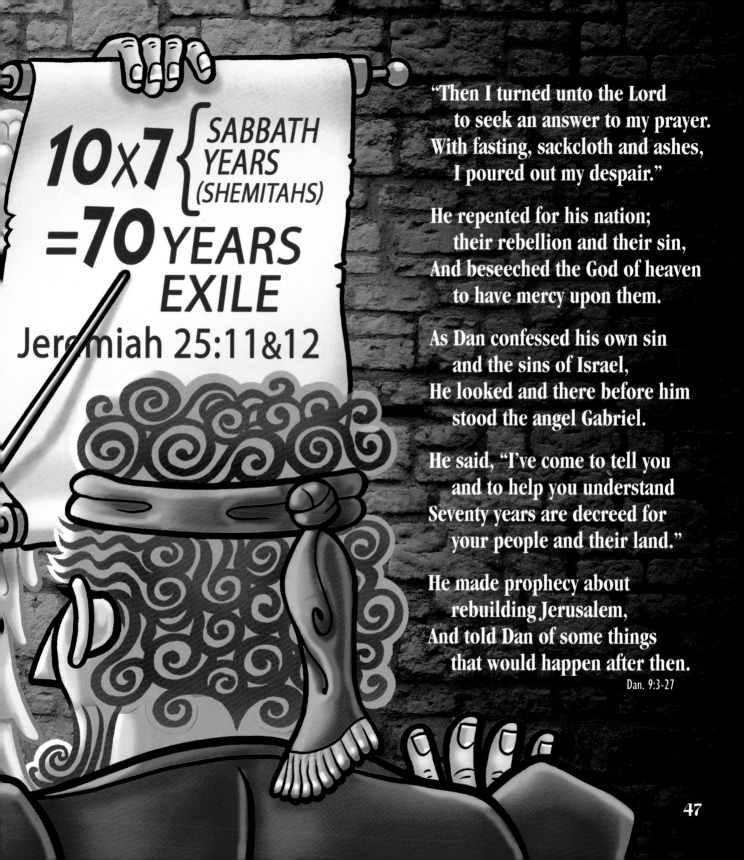

10x7 { SABBATH YEARS (SHEMITAHS)

=70 YEARS EXILE

Jeremiah 25:11&12

"Then I turned unto the Lord
to seek an answer to my prayer.
With fasting, sackcloth and ashes,
I poured out my despair."

He repented for his nation;
their rebellion and their sin,
And beseeched the God of heaven
to have mercy upon them.

As Dan confessed his own sin
and the sins of Israel,
He looked and there before him
stood the angel Gabriel.

He said, "I've come to tell you
and to help you understand
Seventy years are decreed for
your people and their land."

He made prophecy about
rebuilding Jerusalem,
And told Dan of some things
that would happen after then.

Dan. 9:3-27

The last vision that he had is told in chapters ten through twelve,
And as to all its meaning, we cannot begin to delve.

But the lessons from his life that apply to you and me,
Are to always look to God and to serve Him faithfully!